618·97 AUD

D0528134

Introduction

1. In January 2000, the Audit Commission published a report on mental health services for older people entitled *Forget Me Not*[1]. The report set out the Commission's analysis of the state of these services, based on visits to 12 areas, and made 17 key recommendations [**EXHIBIT 1**]. Since its publication, auditors appointed by the Audit Commission have been carrying out local audits of mental health services for older people, using a methodology based on *Forget Me Not* in a much wider range of areas in England and Wales. This has allowed the Commission to assemble a much fuller information base. This update reports the findings for England; a separate paper reports the findings for Wales, where there is a different set of policies.

2. A single team audited all the agencies within each health authority area in England – the health authority itself (including its primary care groups), the local authority(ies), and trust(s) providing mental health services for older people (including primary care trusts). Each area is required to prepare a joint investment plan (JIP) for older people each year. In some places, where services are planned on smaller geographic areas, the agencies choose to produce more than one plan – for example, for each local authority or primary care trust area. Auditors prepared a separate report for each JIP area. This update summarises the main findings of the audits in around 70 JIP areas in England under five headings, derived from the main chapters of *Forget Me Not*:

- in the early stages;
- once specialist help becomes necessary;
- those who can no longer cope at home;
- managing the complexity; and
- drawing the elements together at a strategic level.

3. Most of the fieldwork for the audits was undertaken during 2000, with some continuing into 2001, and so the audits pre-dated the publication of the *National Service Framework for Older People*[II] (NSF) in March 2001 [**BOX A**]. They provide extended information [**BOX B**] which confirms the conclusions of *Forget Me Not*. They also provide a baseline for any future monitoring of progress with the implementation of the NSF.

4. The audits found very wide variations in practice and provision of mental health services for older people across England. Many areas have a lot to do to implement the NSF. This update indicates the magnitude of the task ahead in an area of rapid change. It highlights for managers and practitioners where they should concentrate their efforts.

I   Audit Commission, *Forget Me Not: Mental Health Services for Older People*, Audit Commission, 2000

II   Department of Health, *National Service Framework for Older People*, Department of Health, 2001

EXHIBIT 1

Key recommendations from Forget Me Not

To improve the help given to older people with mental health problems.

In the early stages:

1 GPs and other primary care staff should provide information, support and competent advice.

2 Information about the services available locally, presented in a way that can be understood easily by local people, should be distributed to GP surgeries and other public places.

3 Local mental health professionals should provide training and support for GPs and primary care teams, making particular efforts to contact those that make very few referrals.

Once specialist help becomes necessary, a range of services is needed, including:

4 Where possible members of a community mental health team (CMHT), should carry out an assessment, at home on at least one occasion.

5 Provision balanced in favour of home-based services.

6 A range of specialist community-based staff – ideally with specialist home-care workers. Service managers should consider training home-care staff who express an interest in developing skills in this area.

7 Day provision for time-limited assessment and treatment (day hospitals) as well as long-term care (day centres), with an appropriate mix of staff to meet needs, and planned jointly by health and social care agencies.

8 Respite care in a range of settings, including at home, with some places reserved for emergency situations.

Those who can no longer cope at home need:

9 Hospital admission for people with psychiatric and behavioural problems that cannot be managed in any other setting, with close links to physical health care services – with admissions limited by effective community services.

10 Residential and nursing homes, supported by mental health specialists, to enable them to care for highly dependent individuals, and with a strong emphasis on quality.

11 NHS-funded continuing care for those in greatest need, as determined jointly by health and social services agencies.

Such complexity needs to be managed through:

12 Good co-ordination between health and social care, with integrated teams of professionals who have ready access to a range of flexible services.

13 Effective care planning for individuals, through the Care Programme Approach or a similar method.

14 Effective information sharing between practitioners, preferably with shared files.

All the elements of a comprehensive service need to be drawn together at a strategic level with:

15 Clear goals, including the intended balance between home-based, day, outpatient and hospital services.

16 Good quality information to inform planning, including monitoring of service quality.

17 An approach that promotes innovation and works towards jointly commissioned services by health and local authorities, as emphasised by national policy.

Source: Audit Commission Briefing, January 2000: Forget Me Not

BOX A

National Service Framework (NSF) for Older People

The NSF as a whole, and Standard Seven in particular, support and reinforce the messages in *Forget Me Not*. The aim of Standard Seven is: 'To promote good mental health in older people and to treat and support those older people with dementia and depression'. The standard itself is that: 'Older people who have mental health problems have access to integrated mental health services, provided by the NHS and councils to ensure effective diagnosis, treatment and support, for them and their carers.'

The NHS and councils should find that the results and action plans from their local audits assist them to implement Standard Seven and to carry out the required reviews of:

- the local system of mental health services for older people;
- current arrangements for the management of depression and dementia; and
- current arrangements for the management of dementia in younger people.

Where appropriate, reference is made in this update to related parts of the NSF.

BOX B

Local audits

The local audits involved a range of investigations, including:

- interviews with staff;
- reviews of case files;
- collection of user profile information;
- a survey of all the GPs in each joint investment plan (JIP) area, concerning their views on the diagnosis and management of dementia and depression in older people; and
- a survey of a sample of carers of people with dementia in each JIP area, concerning their experience of services and those of their relative or friend.

This update draws on the responses of 8051 GPs in 73 JIP areas and of 5184 carers in 65 JIP areas.

1

In the early stages

Initial diagnosis

Dementia

Not all GPs agreed that an early diagnosis of dementia was desirable

5.   People with dementia, and those caring for them, often first seek help from their GP. They are often bewildered and confused, and good timely advice is necessary if they are to continue to cope. But GPs across the country differed in the extent to which they felt an early diagnosis was necessary or desirable. In one joint investment plan (JIP) area nearly 90 per cent of GPs felt it was important, while in another area only 20 per cent did so. The greatest variations were in the north of England. The average (mean) for England as a whole was 60 per cent [EXHIBIT 2]. People therefore received a different response depending on which GP they saw and where they lived. A number of trust and social services staff expressed their concern about the delay by some GPs in identifying mental health problems in older people. They said that situations often reached crisis point before specialist services were alerted. Early diagnosis allows treatment with anti-dementia drugs in accordance with the guidelines set by the National Institute for Clinical Excellence.

> **Recommended: that GP practices make increased efforts to diagnose dementia early.**

National Service Framework (NSF) 7.35: 'For older people with suspected dementia, early diagnosis gives access to treatment, allows planning for future care, and helps individuals and their families come to terms with the prognosis.'

Initial diagnosis – dementia

EXHIBIT 2

Early diagnosis of dementia

On average, fewer than two-thirds of GPs felt an early diagnosis was important

Source: Auditors' surveys of 8051 GPs in 73 areas

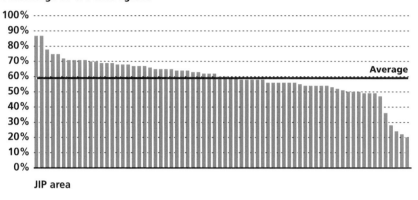

Percentage of GPs who agreed

Average

JIP area

The majority of GPs did not use assessment scales to aid diagnosis

6. Assessment scales may aid the diagnosis of dementia by providing standard questions and ways to score them. Applied appropriately, they can indicate the possible severity of cognitive impairment. However, the majority of GPs were not using such scales [EXHIBIT 3]. These GPs would have had less information with which to judge the extent of people's cognitive impairment. The NSF requires primary care trusts (PCTs) to ensure that, by April 2004, every general practice is using a locally agreed protocol to diagnose, treat and care for patients with depression and dementia.

> **Recommended: that local mental health professionals offer guidance to GPs and primary care staff in the use of assessment scales with dementia.**

> **NSF 7.37: 'Initial diagnosis of dementia involves: ...using assessment scales to aid diagnosis to estimate the severity of cognitive impairment where there is sensitivity to asking direct questions about memory.'**

Most carers recalled a physical examination

7. When a person becomes confused, it is important to look for, and if possible treat, any physical problems that may be contributing to or causing the confusion. It was not possible for auditors to check directly whether a physical examination had taken place, but in most areas, more than two-thirds of carers reported that their relative or friend had been examined by a doctor early on [EXHIBIT 4]. This still left nearly a third of carers who were unsure whether their relative or friend had been examined. However, auditors were not able to corroborate carers' views of whether a physical examination had actually taken place with medical records.

> **Recommended: that GPs systematically assess for physical conditions which may contribute to confusion.**

> **NSF 7.37: 'Initial diagnosis of dementia involves: ...carrying out a physical examination and investigations such as blood and urine tests.'**

Initial diagnosis – dementia

EXHIBIT 3

Use by GPs of specific tests or protocols to detect dementia

Fewer than half of GPs used specific tests or protocols

Source: Auditors' surveys of 8051 GPs in 73 areas

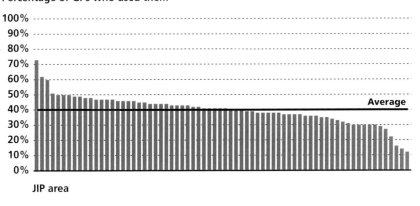

Percentage of GPs who used them

EXHIBIT 4

Carers reporting that their relatives/friends had been examined by a doctor

In most areas over two-thirds of carers recalled a physical examination

Source: Auditors' surveys of 5184 carers in 65 areas

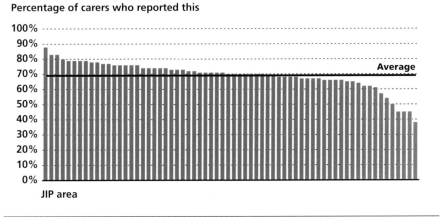

Percentage of carers who reported this

Depression

Nearly all GPs agreed that an early
diagnosis of depression is desirable…

8. Depression is the most common mental health problem in older
people and GPs are often the first point of contact for someone with
suspected depression. In contrast to dementia, most GPs felt that it was
important to look actively for early signs of depression in older people.
But in one area, more than a third of GPs did not agree [EXHIBIT 5]. Despite
these findings, it has been found that depression in older people is
frequently under-detected and untreated in primary care.

> **Recommended: that GPs make increased efforts to diagnose and
> treat depression in older people.**

> **NSF 7.27: 'The treatment of depression involves: making the
> diagnosis and giving the person an explanation of their symptoms.'**

…but again, the majority of GPs did
not use assessment scales to aid
diagnosis

9. Assessment scales may also aid the diagnosis of depression. However,
only a little over a third of GPs were using them [EXHIBIT 6]. Therefore most
GPs could not use such scales to help them diagnose depression or
monitor progress. This is a significant area for development almost
everywhere in England.

> **Recommended: that local mental health professionals offer
> guidance to GPs and primary care staff in the use of assessment
> scales with depression.**

> **NSF 7.24: 'The diagnosis of depression involves an assessment of
> psychiatric, psychological and social factors. This means: …using
> assessment scales to aid diagnosis.'**

Initial diagnosis – depression

EXHIBIT 5

Early diagnosis of depression

The vast majority of GPs felt an early diagnosis was important

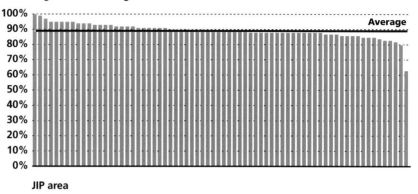

Percentage of GPs who agreed

JIP area

Source: Auditors' surveys of 8051 GPs in 73 areas

EXHIBIT 6

Use by GPs of specific tests or protocols to detect depression

Only a minority of GPs used specific tests or protocols

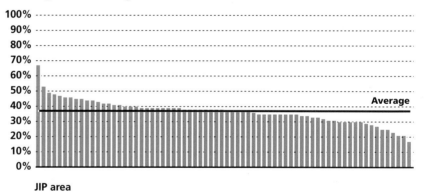

Percentage of GPs who agreed

JIP area

Source: Auditors' surveys of 8051 GPs in 73 areas

Information for older people

FMN 2. Information about the services available locally, presented in a way that can be understood easily by local people, should be distributed to GP surgeries and other public places.

> Once a diagnosis was made, most carers were told what was wrong…

10. Clear information needs to be presented in ways that are easily understood by local older people and their carers. In almost all areas, a high percentage of carers of someone who was forgetful or confused said that they had been told what was wrong with their relative or friend [EXHIBIT 7]. The findings from the local audits were therefore positive. However, most of these carers were already known to the statutory services. The local audits were not able to explore how many carers of people not referred for services had been told. Nor did they explore how many older people with dementia had had the diagnosis explained to them.

NSF 7.39: 'Treatment of dementia always involves: explaining the diagnosis to the older person and any carers and where possible giving relevant information about sources of help and support.'

> …but fewer were told what to expect

11. Significantly fewer carers said that they had been told how their relative's or friend's problems were likely to develop. This information is necessary to help carers prepare and adjust. But, obligations around patient confidentiality can make this a complex area. And GPs often struggle to find the time. It may be better for other members of the primary care team to undertake this task. There were only two areas – both in the north of England – where more than three-quarters of carers said that they had been told [EXHIBIT 8].

Recommended: that current local practice and procedures for explaining to older people with dementia and their carers how the problems are likely to develop are reviewed.

NSF 7.39: 'Treatment of dementia always involves: …giving information about the likely prognosis and options for packages of care.'

Information for older people

EXHIBIT 7

Carers reporting that they had been told what was wrong

Overall, about 90 per cent had been told what was wrong

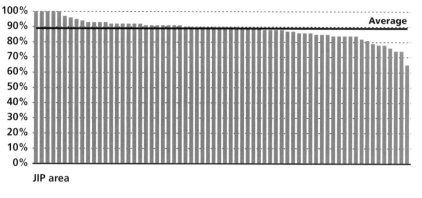

Percentage of carers who reported this

Source: Auditors' surveys of 5184 carers in 65 areas

EXHIBIT 8

Carers reporting that they had been told how their relative's/friend's problems were likely to develop

Fewer than two-thirds recalled being told how things would develop

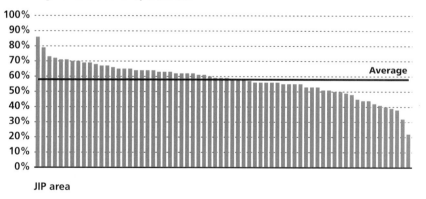

Percentage of carers who reported this

Source: Auditors' surveys of 8051 GPs in 73 areas

Most carers were told how to access help…

12. Around three-quarters of carers of someone who was forgetful or confused said that they had been told what help was available [EXHIBIT 9] and what benefits or allowances could be claimed [EXHIBIT 10].

Information for older people

EXHIBIT 9

Carers reporting that they had been told what help was available

On average about three-quarters had been told about help available

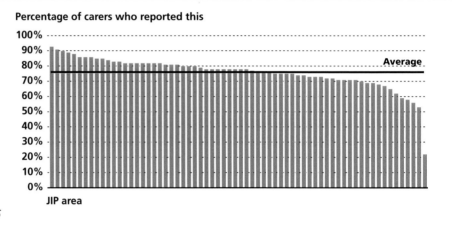

Percentage of carers who reported this

Source: Auditors' surveys of 5184 carers in 65 areas

EXHIBIT 10

Carers reporting that they had been told about benefits/allowances that could be claimed

On average, about three-quarters had been told about the benefits and allowances available

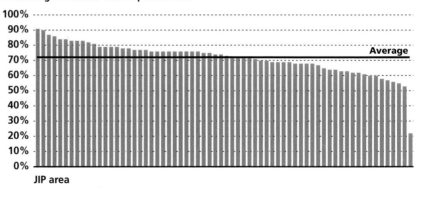

Percentage of carers who reported this

Source: Auditors' surveys of 5184 carers in 65 areas

13. Around two-thirds of carers said that they had been told whether any help would have to be paid for [EXHIBIT 11]. A little over a half said that they knew how to go about getting a place for their relative or friend in a nursing or residential home if he or she should ever need it [EXHIBIT 12].

Information for older people

EXHIBIT 11

Carers reporting that they had been told whether any help would have to be paid for

Around two-thirds were told

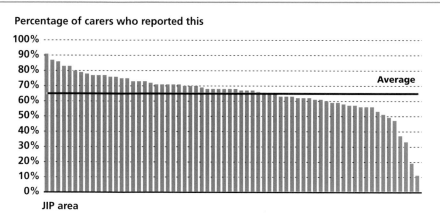

Percentage of carers who reported this

Source: Auditors' surveys of 5184 carers in 65 areas

EXHIBIT 12

Carers reporting that they knew how to get a place in a nursing/residential home

A little over a half knew how to get a place

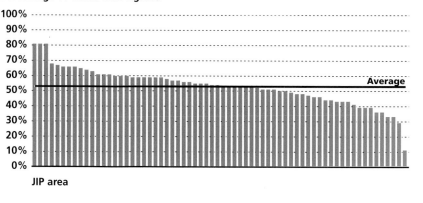

Percentage of carers who agreed

Source: Auditors' surveys of 5184 carers in 65 areas

15

Written information was not always available

14. The figures indicated that significant numbers of carers still need more help with these matters. This was a cause for concern, given that these responses were largely from carers already known to the statutory services. Indeed, auditors identified that information was consistently available, comprehensive, and produced in several languages or alternative media, such as tapes and videos, in only just over a quarter of areas [EXHIBIT 13]. Telephone helplines, including NHS Direct and Care Direct, can play a useful role. The NSF requires all health and social care services to review the information they provide on older people's services, and the formats in which it is available, by April 2002.

15. Voluntary organisations often play a significant role in this area. Alzheimer's Society, through its network of over 200 branches and support groups, provides considerable information and support to people with dementia and carers. Some carers clearly benefit greatly from the structured education courses which have been developed in different locations. The Mental Health Foundation is currently supporting six two-year pilot services for providing information, advice and support to people in the early stages of dementia and their families (four in England and one each in Wales and Scotland)[1]. In addition to these core services the pilots offer befriending, and help with accessing social, health and legal services. An independent evaluation of these pilots has been commissioned, with a view to producing guidelines for the wider development of such services.

> **Recommended: that local areas strengthen arrangements for giving information to service users and their carers.**

> **NSF 7.39: 'The treatment of dementia always involves: explaining the diagnosis to the older person and any carers and where possible giving relevant information about sources of help and support.'**

---

1   A Milne and J Lingard, *The Dementia Advice and Support Service: A Service Development Initiative for People in the Early Stages of Dementia and their Families*, Journal of Dementia Care, 2001, Vol 9.3: pp28-30.

Information for older people

EXHIBIT 13

Availability of written information

Readily available and comprehensive in around a quarter of areas

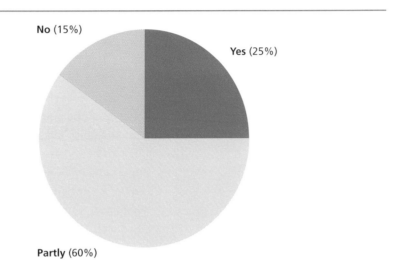

No (15%)

Yes (25%)

Partly (60%)

Source: Audit findings from 61 areas

GP training

FMN 3. Local mental health professionals should provide training and support for GPs and primary care teams, making particular efforts to contact those who refer very few people.

GPs' views: dementia

> The majority of GPs have not been trained to diagnose and manage dementia…

16. In most areas fewer than half of GPs said they had received sufficient training to help them diagnose and manage dementia [**EXHIBIT 14A**]. There was a predominantly positive response from GPs in only six areas. GPs who said they had received sufficient training were significantly more likely to believe in the value of an early diagnosis[1]. It is particularly important that GPs without sufficient training have ready access, when required, to specialist advice. On average fewer than two-thirds felt supported, although the response varied considerably [**EXHIBIT 14B**].

GP training – dementia

EXHIBIT 14A

GPs agreeing that they had received sufficient basic and post-qualifying training for dementia

In most areas fewer than half felt they had sufficient training

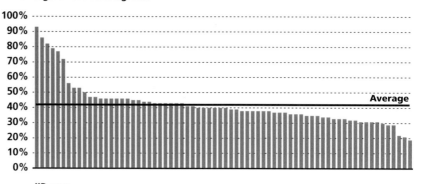

Percentage of GPs who agreed

JIP area

EXHIBIT 14B

GPs agreeing that they had ready access to specialist advice for dementia

Fewer than two-thirds felt they had ready access to specialist advice

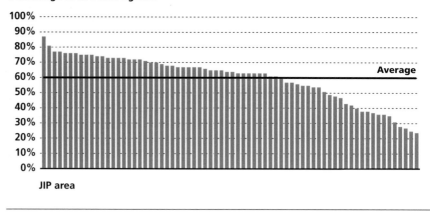

Percentage of GPs who agreed

JIP area

Source: Auditors' surveys of 8051 GPs in 73 areas

I   1 per cent significance using the Spearman Rank Correlation Coefficient

GPs' views: depression

17. Overall, around two-thirds of GPs said they had received sufficient training to help them diagnose and manage depression [EXHIBIT 15A]. This still highlights a need for more training for this common, serious and treatable condition. Just under two-thirds said that they had ready access, when required, to specialist advice. Again this varied quite considerably [EXHIBIT 15B].

...while more have been trained to diagnose and manage depression

GP training – depression

EXHIBIT 15A

GPs agreeing that they had received sufficient basic and post-qualifying training for depression

Overall, around two-thirds felt that they had received sufficient training

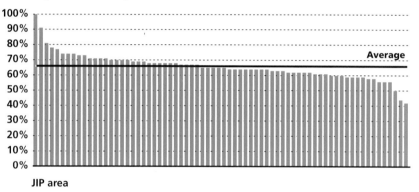

Percentage of GPs who agreed

EXHIBIT 15B

GPs agreeing that they had ready access to specialist advice for depression

Just under two-thirds felt they had access to specialist help

Source: Auditors' surveys of 8051 GPs in 73 areas

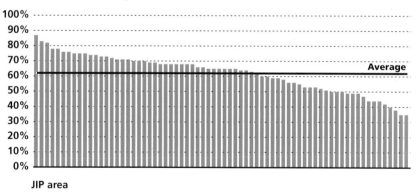

Percentage of GPs who agreed

Support and guidance

18. Clearly, GPs feel the need for more support and guidance from specialist services. And yet only one in ten specialist services was monitoring GP referrals consistently, and making efforts to get in touch with those who referred very few people. Also comprehensive training and support for GPs was only consistently available in around 15 per cent of areas, and not available at all in over 40 per cent of them [EXHIBIT 16]. This is therefore a major area for development.

19. Further analysis of the data that informed *Forget Me Not* indicated that, where local mental health professionals had made specific efforts to contact GPs and provided them with specialist advice, the GPs were more likely to believe in the value of early diagnosis of dementia[I]. The multi-centre collaborative three-year randomised controlled trial, led by the University of Bradford's Dementia Group, is exploring three different formats for training GPs and practice nurses about dementia; findings will be available later in 2002[II].

> **Few specialist services monitor GP referrals or provide training**

> **Recommended: that specialist services review their local arrangements for monitoring referrals from GPs, contacting those who make very few. Also that they review arrangements for training and supporting GPs and primary care teams in the diagnosis and management of dementia and depression where appropriate.**

> **NSF 7.54: 'Specialist mental health teams should work with primary care trainers to develop training in: at least one screen for cognitive impairment, one depression screen, and assessment of suicide risk.'**

> **NSF 7.56: 'Specialist mental health services for older people should provide advice and outreach to those providing: primary care.'**

I   J Renshaw, P Scurfield, L Cloke and M Orrell, *'General practitioners' views on the early diagnosis of dementia'*, British Journal of General Practice, vol. 51, 2001, pp37-38.

II   M Downs and S Iliffe (principal investigators), *Improving the Response of Primary Care Practitioners to People with Dementia and their Families: A Randomised Controlled Trial of Educational Interventions, 1999-2002*, funded by Alzheimer's Society.

GP training – support and guidance

EXHIBIT 16

Support for GPs from specialist services.

Only one in ten specialist services is monitoring referrals and one in six providing comprehensive training and support

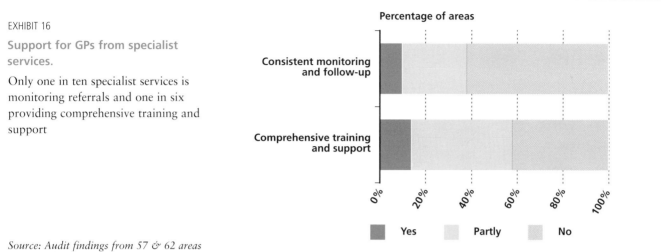

Percentage of areas

Source: Audit findings from 57 & 62 areas respectively

2

Once specialist help becomes necessary

Specialist mental health team assessment

> Most first assessments were carried out at home

FMN 4. Where possible, assessment should take place by members of a community mental health team at home on at least one occasion.

20. If people with mental health problems are to be supported at home successfully, comprehensive assessment of their needs is an essential first step. It is often preferable that this takes place at home – where they, and any carers, are likely to behave and communicate normally, and where staff are best able to gain an accurate view of their needs. In three-quarters of areas most first assessments were carried out at home, although an analysis of the full situation and a prognosis was done in only 60 per cent of areas [EXHIBIT 17]. It is recognised that this is not possible in emergency situations.

21. By April 2002, a single assessment process is to be introduced for the health and social care of older people. This is a milestone for Standard Two of the NSF. It should ensure that there is always an appropriate assessment of a person's situation. The assessment tools and training of assessors must include the needs of older people with mental health problems. And data protection issues must be addressed and resolved.

NSF 2.27: 'The NHS Plan proposed a single assessment process across health and social care for older people. Implementing this should ensure that: a more standardised assessment process is in place across all areas and agencies; standards of assessment practice are raised; older people's needs are assessed in the round.'

EXHIBIT 17

Assessments at home

Home assessments were routine in three in four areas, but involved a full analysis in only three in five

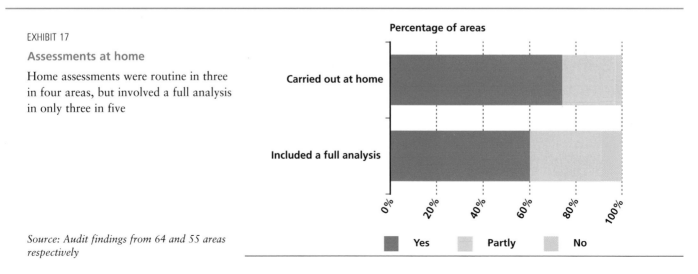

Percentage of areas

Carried out at home

Included a full analysis

0% 20% 40% 60% 80% 100%

■ Yes   Partly   No

Source: Audit findings from 64 and 55 areas respectively

Care at home

Home care was not always available out of hours

22. Most of the expenditure on specialist mental health care for older people goes on hospital, nursing home and residential care. But most people prefer to be supported in their own home. Voluntary organisations often play a significant role in facilitating this. *Forget Me Not* recommended that agencies should consider a shift in balance towards community-based care.

23. Auditors found substantial variations in the reported spending on community-based services. These variations were undoubtedly reflected in the nature and extent of the service provision in different areas. For example, evening and weekend home care was consistently provided in around three-quarters of areas, but night home care was consistently available in fewer than a half of them [EXHIBIT 18].

> **Recommended: that agencies give further consideration to developing home orientated care.**

NSF 7.51: 'Patients with complex mental health needs can and should be treated and supported in the community and wherever practicable at home.'

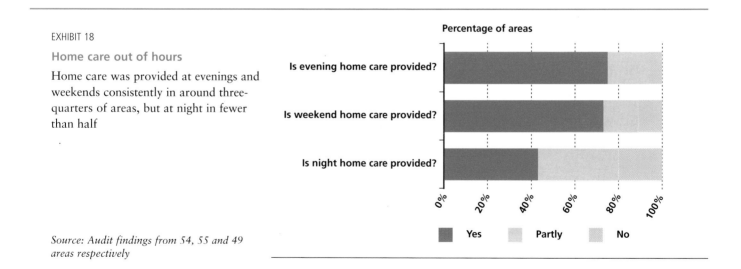

EXHIBIT 18

Home care out of hours

Home care was provided at evenings and weekends consistently in around three-quarters of areas, but at night in fewer than half

Source: Audit findings from 54, 55 and 49 areas respectively

Community-based staff

Not all areas had specialist multi-disciplinary teams...

24. A specialist mental health team is usually at the core of the specialist service for older people with mental health problems. But, auditors reported that specialist multidisciplinary teams existed in fewer than half the areas, although they did partly exist in a further third [EXHIBIT 19]. Areas without such teams will struggle to implement a single assessment process for older people with mental health problems. This contrasts with the situation reported in *Forget Me Not*, where two-thirds of study sites had specialist multidisciplinary teams.

> **Recommended: that agencies consider setting up specialist mental health teams for older people if they don't already have them.**

...and the mix of professionals on the teams varied widely

25. The number and mix of specialist staff in specialist teams varied considerably. Community psychiatric/mental health nurses were most commonly present, followed by occupational therapists, social workers, consultant old age psychiatrists and clinical psychologists [EXHIBIT 20]. However, the number of staff present from each profession (per 10,000 population over 65) varied between areas in every region by at least a factor of four.

> **Recommended: that agencies in each area jointly review the composition of specialist teams, and adjust it where necessary.**

NSF 7.47: 'Core members of the specialist mental health service should include: consultant psychiatrists specialising in mental health problems in old age; community mental health nurses; clinical psychologists; occupational therapists; social workers.'

Few areas had home-care workers trained in mental health

26. Home care is one of the key services for supporting older people with mental health problems at home, provided it is given flexibly and sensitively. However, auditors found home-care workers with additional training in mental health in only one in seven areas [EXHIBIT 21]. This contrasted with the situation in the original 12 study sites where they existed in 5 sites – which were the same 5 sites where more GPs said that local services for older people with dementia and depression were satisfactory.

> **Recommended: that agencies should provide training programmes in mental health for home-care workers.**

Community-based staff

EXHIBIT 19

Areas with specialist multidisciplinary teams for older people

Fewer than half of areas were fully covered

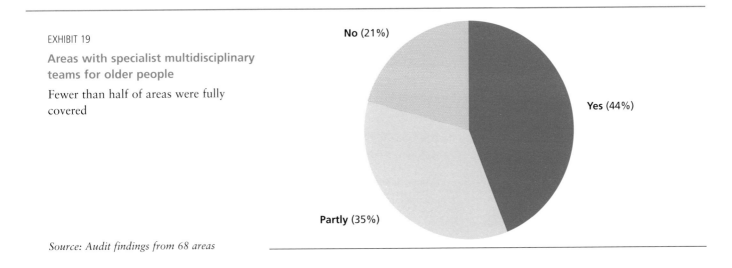

No (21%)

Yes (44%)

Partly (35%)

Source: Audit findings from 68 areas

EXHIBIT 20

Professionals on specialist teams

The number and mix of staff varied considerably

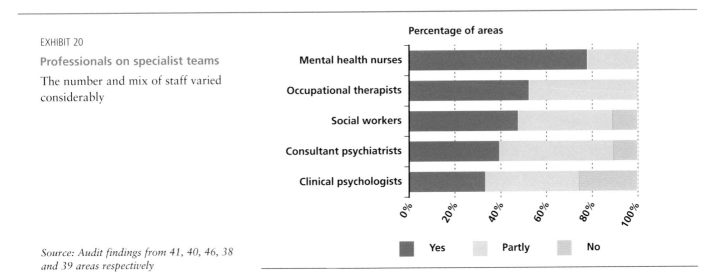

Percentage of areas

Mental health nurses
Occupational therapists
Social workers
Consultant psychiatrists
Clinical psychologists

0% 20% 40% 60% 80% 100%

■ Yes   Partly   No

Source: Audit findings from 41, 40, 46, 38 and 39 areas respectively

EXHIBIT 21

Home-care workers trained in mental health

Trained home-care staff were consistently available in only one in seven areas

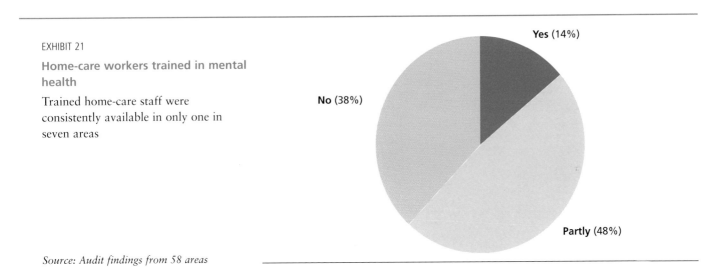

Yes (14%)

No (38%)

Partly (48%)

Source: Audit findings from 58 areas

Day provision

FMN 7. Day provision should be made for time-limited assessment and treatment (day hospitals) as well as long-term care (day centres), with an appropriate mix of staff to meet needs. It should be planned jointly by health and social care agencies.

Almost all areas had day hospitals but the scope of their services varied

27. In most areas, both the NHS and social care agencies (statutory, voluntary and/or private) provided day services. The NHS provided day services in day hospitals, and social care agencies provided them in the community, usually in day centres. Auditors also found increasing instances where day services were being provided jointly.

28. However, the nature and extent of these day services varied considerably between different areas. Generally there was at least one day hospital for older people with mental health problems in each area. But these day hospitals provided comprehensive assessments and short-term treatment in fewer than half the areas. Also specialist memory clinics and access to appropriate therapies for people who had functional mental illnesses were available across less than half the areas [EXHIBIT 22].

NSF 7.49: 'Hospital-based services provided by the specialist mental health services should include: ...day hospitals to offer intensive treatment to people with functional disorders and dementia, including aftercare following in-patient admissions and rehabilitation and support for older people with long-term mental illness such as schizophrenia; memory clinics.'

NSF 7.27: 'The treatment of depression involves: ...offering psychological therapies alongside antidepressant treatment.'

Specialist day centres were less common

29. Specialist long-term day care was not available in all areas, and particularly not for older people with functional mental illnesses which is a long-standing need. And, where it was provided, it was often not available before 10am or after 4pm or at weekends [EXHIBIT 23].

30. The amount of specialist day services (per 10,000 population over 65) provided by the NHS and by social care agencies in each region varied by a factor of at least two between different areas, and often by much more.

> **Recommended: that the agencies in each area review local day provision for older people with mental health problems.**

> **NSF 7.51: 'Community-based mental health services should include: ...day care, providing a range of stimulating group and one to one activities.'**

Day provision

EXHIBIT 22

Specialist day hospital(s)

Most areas had a specialist day hospital, but fewer than half provided consistent access to services

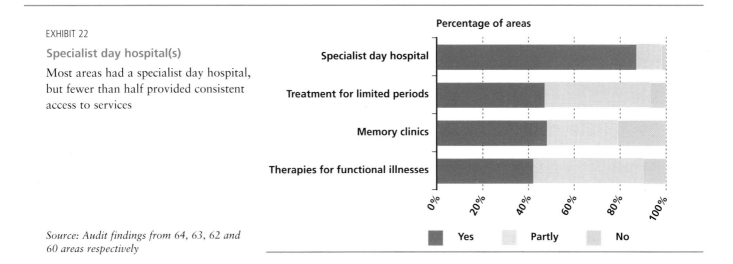

Source: Audit findings from 64, 63, 62 and 60 areas respectively

EXHIBIT 23

Specialist long-term day care

Day care was not consistently available; and not widely available at less social hours

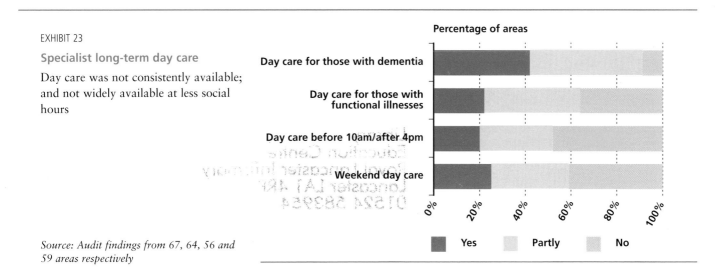

Source: Audit findings from 67, 64, 56 and 59 areas respectively

Respite care

FMN 8. Respite care should be provided in a range of settings, including at home, with some places reserved for emergency situations.

Fewer than two-thirds of carers could get respite care

31. Respite care, to give carers a break, is essential to enable them to continue caring. Carers in the original 12 study sites said it was the service they sought or valued most, and this too was generally found to be the case in the subsequent audits. But on average fewer than two-thirds of carers reported that they could get the help they needed to give them a break, with fewer than half in some areas [EXHIBIT 24]. Support groups for carers existed in almost all areas.

32. The availability of planned respite care varied considerably between areas. It was consistently available in residential and/or nursing homes in nearly two-thirds of areas and in hospital in a little over half [EXHIBIT 25], though the actual amount (per 10,000 population over 65) varied enormously. This left a considerable number of areas where respite care was not available in one or other of these settings, or only available in part of the area.

33. Emergency respite care (within 24 hours) was consistently available in only around half of the areas, and home-based respite, including sitting services, in only a quarter of them [EXHIBIT 26]. Admiral nurses, who specialise in the support of people with dementia and their families, are now employed in 12 areas and are being piloted in a further 3.

> **Recommended: that agencies review with users and carers the provision of respite care.**

NSF 7.52: 'Short-term breaks and other support services should be available for carers of older people with mental health problems, and this should include out of hours and weekend provision.'

Respite care

Carers who could get help to give them a break

On average, slightly fewer than two-thirds could get help

Source: Auditors' surveys of 5184 carers in 65 areas

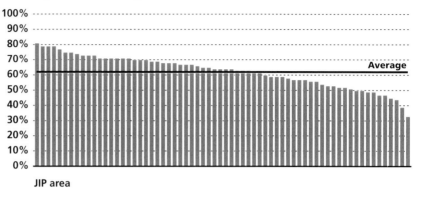

Percentage of carers who agreed

Average

JIP area

Planned respite care in residential/nursing homes, and in hospitals

Respite care was available in residential/nursing homes in nearly two in three areas, and in hospitals in one in two

Source: Audit findings from 61 and 57 areas respectively

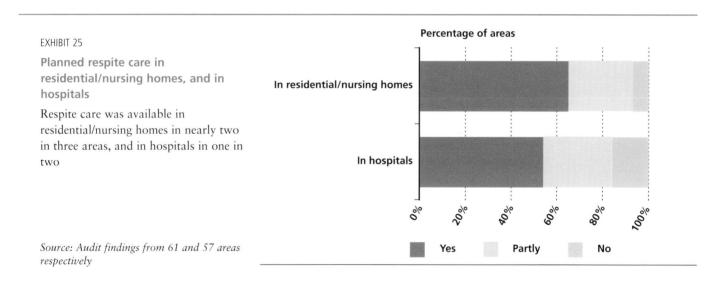

Percentage of areas

In residential/nursing homes

In hospitals

■ Yes   ▨ Partly   ▨ No

Emergency and home-based respite care

Emergency respite care was available in just over half the areas, and home-based respite in a quarter

Source: Audit findings from 46 and 44 areas respectively

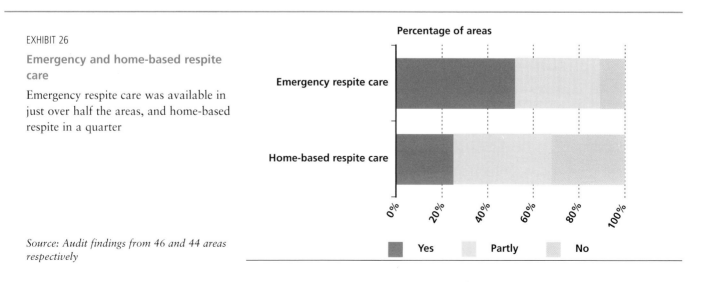

Percentage of areas

Emergency respite care

Home-based respite care

■ Yes   ▨ Partly   ▨ No

3

Those who can no longer cope at home

Hospital care

> FMN 9. Hospital admission is needed for people with psychiatric and behavioural problems that cannot be managed in any other setting, with close links to physical health care services – with admissions limited by effective community services.

| Sometimes people are in hospital because community services are lacking… |

34. Some older people with mental health problems need a spell in hospital to treat a psychiatric or behavioural problem. Auditors confirmed the *Forget Me Not* finding that the number of acute psychiatric beds occupied by older people with dementia (per 10,000 population over 65) varied considerably between areas, as did the average length of stay in these beds. In some areas, the dependency of people with dementia on acute psychiatric wards was low, indicating that the potential of community services was underdeveloped.

> Recommended: agencies review whether it might be possible to maintain more people in community settings.

| …and hospital facilities are not always ideal |

35. It is generally accepted that it is good practice to provide separate areas in acute psychiatric wards for people with dementia and those with functional illnesses, and for frail older people and younger people with functional illnesses. However, auditors found such a separation consistently in only two-fifths of areas, partly so in around a further third and not at all in the remaining quarter [EXHIBIT 27A].

36. Auditors also reported in over one third of areas the physical environments in which respite and hospital services were provided were unsuitable for older people with mental health problems and were consistently suitable in only just over a quarter [EXHIBIT 27B].

> Recommended: commissioners and trusts review how to improve the environments in which mental health services are provided.

37. It is important that both the physical and mental health needs of older people are addressed. Ideally, some mental health beds for older people should be based on the same site as the general hospital. Auditors reported that this happened or partly happened in four out of five areas [EXHIBIT 27C]. However, effective communication, advice and support between staff of the mental health and physical care services can help reduce the problems of physical separation, and are more important.

Hospital care

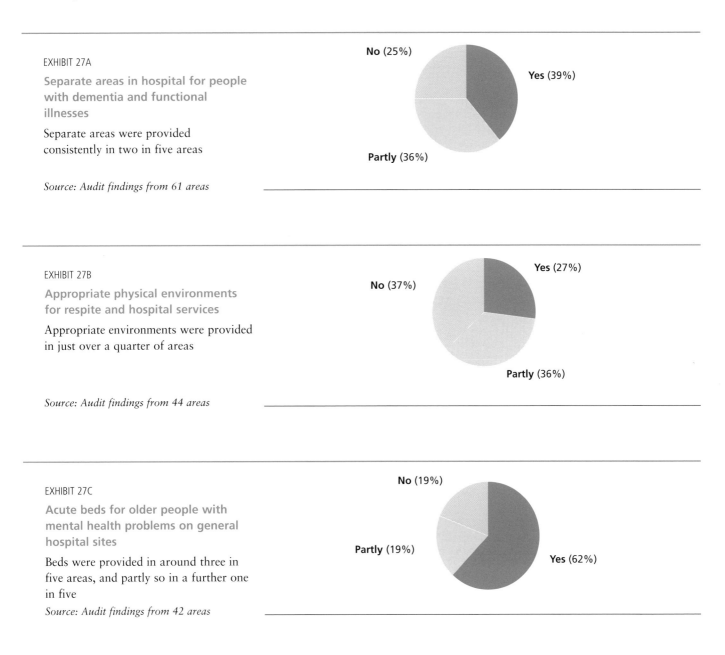

EXHIBIT 27A

Separate areas in hospital for people with dementia and functional illnesses

Separate areas were provided consistently in two in five areas

Source: Audit findings from 61 areas

No (25%)

Yes (39%)

Partly (36%)

EXHIBIT 27B

Appropriate physical environments for respite and hospital services

Appropriate environments were provided in just over a quarter of areas

Source: Audit findings from 44 areas

Yes (27%)

No (37%)

Partly (36%)

EXHIBIT 27C

Acute beds for older people with mental health problems on general hospital sites

Beds were provided in around three in five areas, and partly so in a further one in five

Source: Audit findings from 42 areas

No (19%)

Partly (19%)

Yes (62%)

Residential and nursing home care

FMN 10. Residential and nursing homes are needed, supported by mental health specialists, to enable them to care for highly dependent individuals, with a strong emphasis on quality.

Only two-thirds of areas had specialist homes for people with dementia...

38. The decision to move into a residential or nursing home is one of the most significant taken by any older person. Different homes can provide very different environments. Some specialise in the care of older people with dementia, but it is much less common to find one caring for older people with functional illnesses. Some specialist residential and nursing home care for people with dementia was only consistently available in around two-thirds of areas; and had consistently good quality physical environments in only half [EXHIBIT 28]. Current shortfalls in residential and nursing home provision in some areas are not helping.

> **Recommended: that commissioners of residential and nursing home care ensure there is sufficient good quality care available for older people with mental health problems including some specialist provision.**

NSF 7.19: 'The NHS and local councils should work with care home providers in their areas to develop a range of services to meet the needs of older people with mental health problems, including specialist residential care places for older people with dementia.'

NSF 7.11: 'Older people in residential care and nursing homes and those receiving day care should be able to participate in a range of stimulating group or one to one activities... An appropriate environment can also aid orientation and help to avoid visual and sensory confusion. This will involve good quality design, lighting, colour contrast and accessible accommodation.'

...and specialist services provided support and training for homes' staff in only a quarter

39. Support, advice and training for staff working in residential and nursing homes, whether or not specialist, about the care of older people with mental health problems can be very beneficial. It can help staff to cope better with difficult situations and help improve residents' quality of life. It may also help to reduce the numbers of residents admitted to hospital or transferred to other homes. However, this kind of support and education was consistently available in only just over a quarter of areas [EXHIBIT 29].

> **Recommended: that each specialist mental health service reviews the advice, support and training provided to homes in its area.**

NSF 7.54: 'Specialist mental health services should provide training and advice for other professionals and staff whose responsibilities include providing care and treatment for older people with mental health problems.'

NSF 7.56: 'Specialist mental health services for older people should provide advice and outreach to those providing: ...residential care and nursing homes, and sheltered housing.'

Residential and nursing home care

EXHIBIT 28

Residential and nursing homes

Some specialist care was available in around two-thirds of areas, with consistent good quality physical environments in around a half

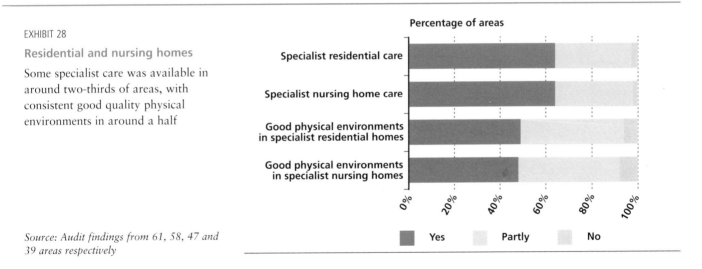

Percentage of areas

Source: Audit findings from 61, 58, 47 and 39 areas respectively

EXHIBIT 29

Support and education to residential and nursing homes and their staff

Support and education were consistently available in a little more than a quarter of areas

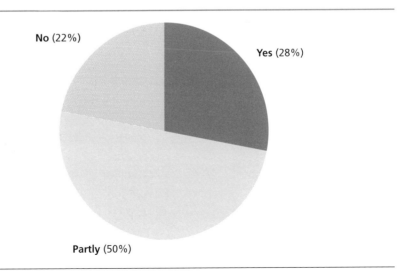

No (22%)

Yes (28%)

Partly (50%)

Source: Audit findings from 60 areas

Continuing care

FMN 11. NHS-funded continuing care is also required for those in greatest need, as determined jointly by health and social services agencies.

NHS-funded continuing care was not available in all areas

40. Health and local authorities in each area are required to establish a continuing care agreement concerning their respective responsibilities for the provision of long-term care, and relevant staff should be aware of its content. Authorities should have reviewed their criteria to ensure compliance with last year's Coughlan judgement. NHS-funded continuing care may be required for those who are the most dependent or whose behaviour is the most challenging.

41. The amount and location of the continuing care provision for older people with mental health problems varied considerably between areas. In over a third of areas, authorities had not reached a comprehensive agreement concerning its provision. It was funded by the NHS in three-quarters of areas for older people with dementia; in around two-thirds for those with functional illnesses; and in just over half for those with challenging behaviour [EXHIBIT 30]. This was an unsatisfactory and inequitable situation – not only for older people and their carers, but also for the agencies themselves.

Recommended: that agencies make every effort to reach a continuing care agreement to which all can subscribe.

Continuing care

EXHIBIT 30

Continuing care

Policies and provision varied

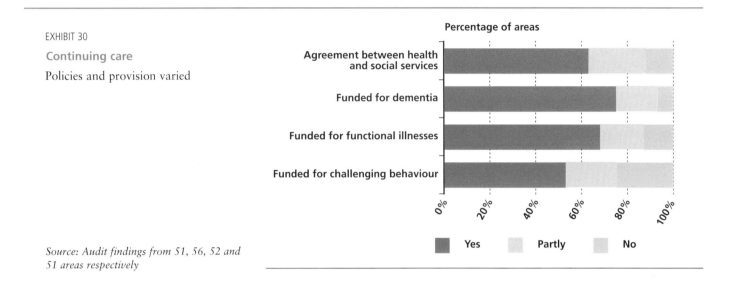

Percentage of areas

Agreement between health and social services

Funded for dementia

Funded for functional illnesses

Funded for challenging behaviour

0% 20% 40% 60% 80% 100%

Yes   Partly   No

Source: Audit findings from 51, 56, 52 and 51 areas respectively

4

Managing the complexity

Co-ordination

FMN 12. Such complexity requires good co-ordination between health and social care, with integrated teams of professionals who have ready access to a range of flexible services.

Health and social care staff need to work together

42. Good co-ordination between health and social care agencies can greatly enhance the quality and effectiveness of services for older people with mental health problems. Auditors reported that in two-fifths of areas most cases were 'jointly worked' between members of the specialist mental health teams, and that in a further two-fifths of areas this was partly so. This kind of working can be facilitated if specialist team members are based in the same office. This happened in around a quarter of areas, and partly so in a further two-fifths [EXHIBIT 31].

43. It is easier to provide co-ordinated care where health and social services staff have easy access to each other's resources. Auditors reported this to be the case in a sixth of areas, and to be the case to some extent in a further half [EXHIBIT 32]. The development and implementation of agreed care pathways can help co-ordinate efficient use of the available resources.

> **Recommended: that agencies work to improve co-ordination between staff.**

Co-ordination

EXHIBIT 31

Co-ordination between health and social care staff

Members worked on cases together in around two-fifths of areas and were based together in one in four

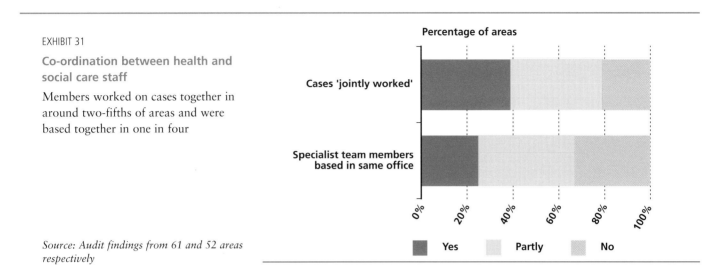

Percentage of areas

Cases 'jointly worked'

Specialist team members based in same office

■ Yes   Partly   ■ No

Source: Audit findings from 61 and 52 areas respectively

EXHIBIT 32

Health and social services staff with easy access to each other's resources

Access was consistent in a sixth of areas and partial in a further half

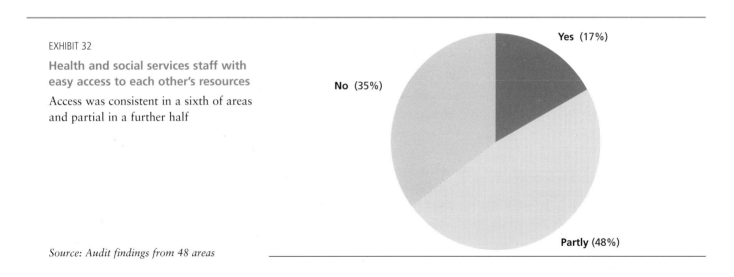

Yes (17%)

No (35%)

Partly (48%)

Source: Audit findings from 48 areas

Care planning

Better care planning is needed…

44. Effective assessment and management of each person's care is essential. Many older people, particularly those with dementia, have complex needs and require both health and social care. Standard, jointly-agreed procedures for assessment and care management were routinely in place in just a third of areas, and partly in place in a further two-fifths. The assessment process was aligned with social services' care management function in around a third of areas, and partly so in just under a further two-fifths [EXHIBIT 33]. Some of the basis for the single assessment process, to be introduced by April 2002, was already in place in around three-quarters of areas. But the agencies in the remaining quarter of areas will require a concerted effort to meet this deadline.

45. The use of key workers can facilitate effective care management. Generally older people with mental health problems had them in four-fifths of areas, and at least some older people in most of the other areas [EXHIBIT 34].

Recommended: that agencies agree assessment and care management procedures.

NSF 7.53: 'A core team member should act as a care co-ordinator for each older person referred to the specialist mental health service throughout his or her contact with the service.'

…and services that are culturally appropriate should be available

46. Care planning can only be effective if services are available that are acceptable and appropriate for each person involved, including those from black and minority ethnic communities. Culturally appropriate services for different groups existed in only 6 per cent of areas, and partly so in a further half [EXHIBIT 35].

Recommended: that agencies develop services which are acceptable and appropriate for people from black and minority ethnic communities.

NSF 7.3: 'Older people from black and minority ethnic communities need accessible and appropriate mental health services.'

Care planning

EXHIBIT 33

Jointly agreed assessment and care management procedures

Around a third of areas had such procedures

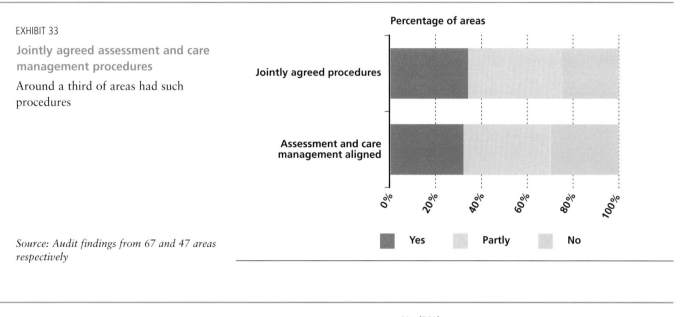

Source: Audit findings from 67 and 47 areas respectively

EXHIBIT 34

Key workers

Key workers were used in nearly all areas

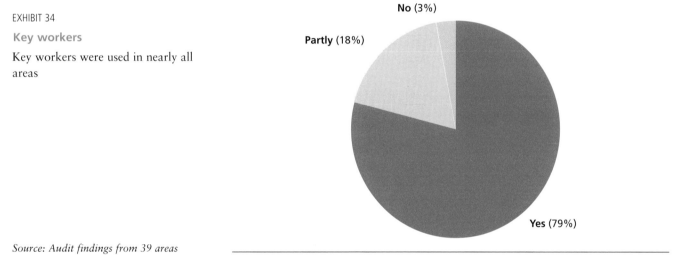

Source: Audit findings from 39 areas

EXHIBIT 35

Culturally appropriate services

Only a small minority of areas had culturally appropriate services, although a further half had them to some degree

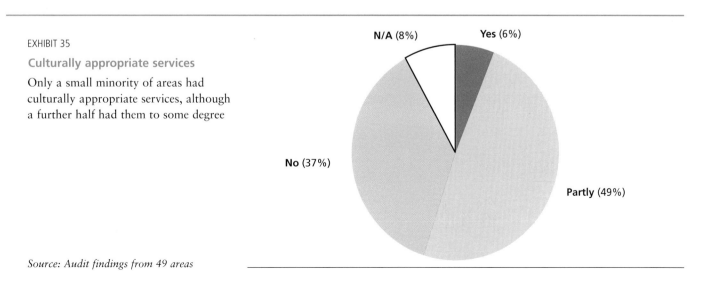

Source: Audit findings from 49 areas

Information sharing

FMN 14. Effective information sharing is also needed between practitioners, preferably with shared files.

Shared case files were rare; and compatible IT systems even rarer

47. Effective information sharing between health and social care practitioners is a prerequisite to successful co-ordination. Joint working and the single assessment process must be weakened without it. However, auditors found that shared case files, or easy access to each other's files, only existed in a tenth of areas, and partly so in only a further third [EXHIBIT 36]. In other words, case notes were not shared in three-fifths of areas. The potential for user-held or carer-held records had not been widely explored.

48. Many agencies have developed, or are in the process of developing, computerised patient or service user records. But auditors reported that health and social services IT systems were compatible in only a few areas [EXHIBIT 37].

49. There was clearly some effective co-ordination, assessment and care management occurring in different places. But the circumstances and relationships in some areas made these more difficult to achieve than in others. Agencies must continue to strive to manage the complexities, so that effective co-ordination and service delivery can be a reality everywhere. The implementation of the Information Strategy for Older People will further support improved working across health and social care agencies.

> **Recommended: that agencies develop effective information sharing and compatible IT systems.**

NSF 7.13: 'Older people with mental health problems are a particularly vulnerable group who may come into contact with a number of health and social services. These agencies should have systems in place to communicate with one another, share information, to understand how and when to refer older people on to appropriate services, and to review the older person's needs as changes in circumstances or conditions arise.'

Information sharing

EXHIBIT 36

EXHIBIT 36

Shared case files

Staff in only a tenth of areas shared files, although there was access in a further third

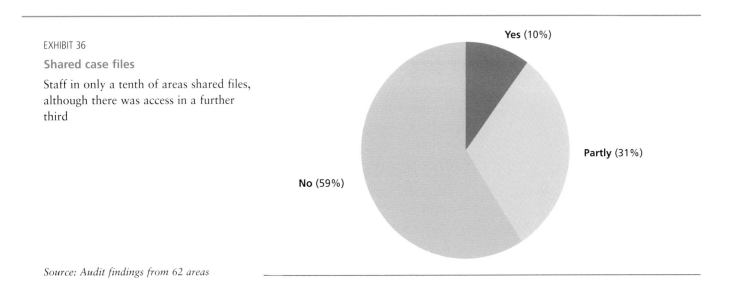

Yes (10%)

Partly (31%)

No (59%)

Source: Audit findings from 62 areas

EXHIBIT 37

IT systems compatible between health and social services

Systems were compatible in very few areas

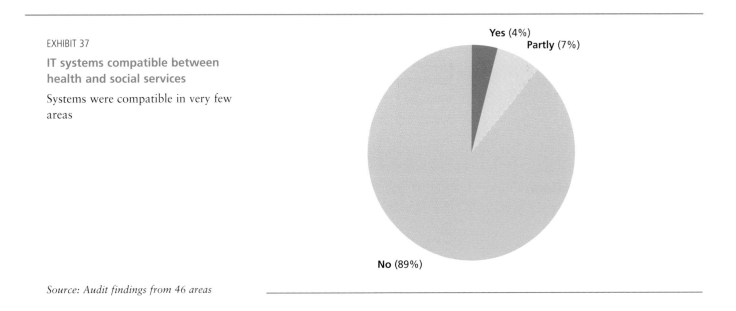

Yes (4%)
Partly (7%)

No (89%)

Source: Audit findings from 46 areas

5 Drawing the elements together at a strategic level

Clear goals

FMN 15. Clear goals are needed, including the intended balance between home-based, day, outpatient, residential and hospital services.

Nearly a quarter of areas had no clear goals…

50. All the elements of a comprehensive service need to be drawn together at a strategic level with clear goals for each element and for the service as a whole – including the intended balance between home-based, day, outpatient, residential and hospital services. Otherwise, services may be poorly targeted and over-burdened, and gaps in provision may be masked. However, auditors found that nearly a quarter of areas had no clear service goals and plans, and were only partly in place in around another third [EXHIBIT 38]. Agencies must also be clear how the needs of younger people with dementia will be met.

Recommended: that agencies in all areas have agreed and clear goals and plans for these services.

Good information

FMN 16. Good quality information is needed to inform planning, including the monitoring of service quality.

…and a third were not making full use of demographic data

51. Good information about local demographics, resources and current services is the starting point for sound future plans. Information about local demographics and current resources was being fully taken into account in around two-thirds of areas [EXHIBIT 39]. But auditors experienced difficulty in confirming the basis on which some agencies reported their current levels of expenditure on mental health services for older people.

Recommended: that agencies make full use of information in developing their plans.

Clear goals

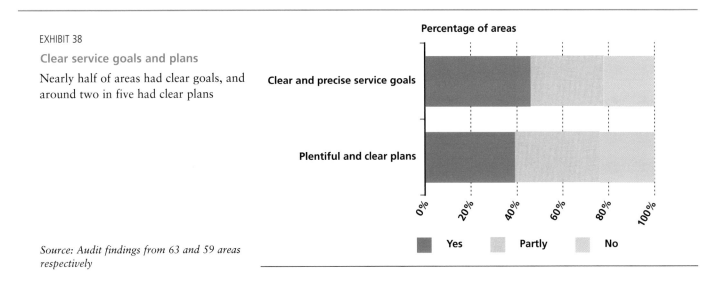

EXHIBIT 38

Clear service goals and plans

Nearly half of areas had clear goals, and around two in five had clear plans

Source: Audit findings from 63 and 59 areas respectively

Good information

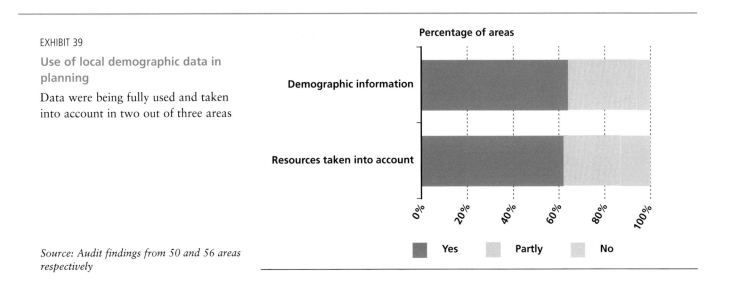

EXHIBIT 39

Use of local demographic data in planning

Data were being fully used and taken into account in two out of three areas

Source: Audit findings from 50 and 56 areas respectively

Joint approach

FMN 17. A comprehensive service also needs an approach that promotes innovation and works towards jointly commissioned services by health and local authorities, as emphasised by national policy.

Joint approaches to planning are required, involving a wide range of participants

52. Appropriate personnel from all relevant agencies and interests should be represented in the local strategic planning of mental health services for older people. However, the appropriate people from health and social services were fully involved in only two-thirds of areas and from the voluntary sector in around a half. GPs and users and carers were only adequately represented in around a half of areas [EXHIBIT 40].

53. During the time that the audits were taking place, auditors found that just over half the agencies were discussing new arrangements for lead purchasing or partial new arrangements. They reported that arrangements were already in place, or partly in place, for pooled budgets between health and social services in around a third of areas [EXHIBIT 41]. This has the potential to facilitate more flexible and responsive services.

54. This is a fast moving area. Joint approaches to the planning, commissioning and delivery of mental health service for older people, including the development of agreed care pathways, will almost certainly have developed further in many areas since the audits were completed. Examples include the integrated care pathway for dementia developed by the Kingshill Research Centre in Swindon,[1] and 'the cash for change' initiative linked with the 'Building Capacity and Partnership in Care' agreement. In some areas new arrangements will now be in place.

> **Recommended: that agencies develop joint plans for commissioning and delivering integrated services involving key partners.**

NSF 7.45: 'Primary Care Groups and Trusts should ensure that there is integrated planning and delivery of local services to support the detection, diagnosis and treatment of mental health problems in primary care. PCG/Ts should be supported by specialist services, where appropriate.'

---

1   M Naido and R Bullock, *An Integrated Care Pathway for Dementia*, Harcourt Health Communications, 2001.

Joint approach

EXHIBIT 40

Joint approaches to planning

Health and social services personnel were fully involved in two out of three areas; people from the voluntary sector, and GPs and users and carers were involved in half

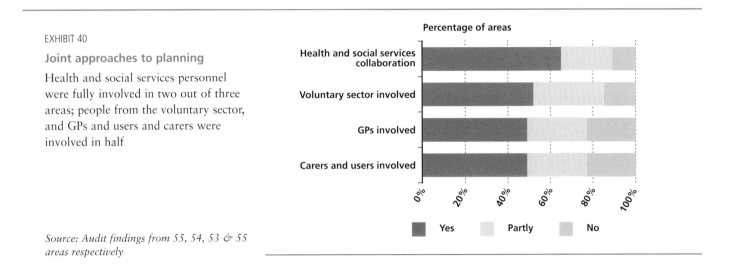

Percentage of areas

Source: Audit findings from 55, 54, 53 & 55 areas respectively

EXHIBIT 41

Lead purchasing and pooled budgets

Agencies were discussing new arrangements for lead purchasing in just over half of areas, and arrangements were in place, or partly so, for pooled budgets in around a third

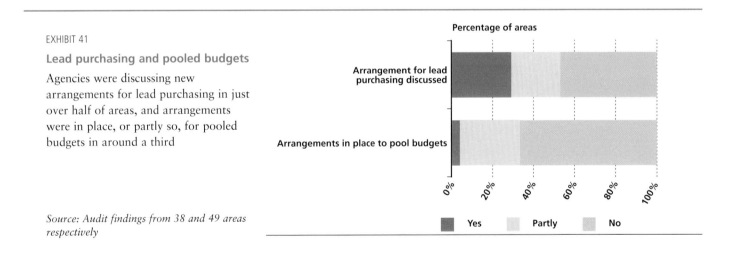

Percentage of areas

Source: Audit findings from 38 and 49 areas respectively

6

Summary overview

55. In the previous pages, the exhibits have shown the variations observed between areas. For each topic, some areas do well while others do less well. But is it the same areas doing well throughout or are all areas doing reasonably well at some things? To test this, a simple scoring system has been devised, and scores calculated for each area for the range of specialist services provided, team work and planning, using most of the charts in this report [BOX C].

56. The values show a wide range of performance [EXHIBIT 42], with some areas scoring well in all areas but others scoring poorly in all areas, and a gradual progression in between. All three scores are highly correlated[I], showing that areas that score highly in one category also score highly in the other two. In other words, areas that have good services also have good co-ordination and strategic planning, and those with poor services have poor co-ordination and strategic planning.

57. Some areas are doing well overall, but some have limited mental health services for older people. Each area has received an individual audit report setting out the issues that it needs to address. All areas have been encouraged to produce an action plan agreed between agencies. Where performance is poor, the introduction of the NSF provides a new impetus for areas to take this action plan forward with some urgency. Areas throughout the country are encouraged to use the information in this report and their individual audits to strengthen their services as necessary.

I   Each pair correlate with 1 per cent significance using the Spearman Rank Correlation Coefficient

Overall scoring

EXHIBIT 42

Total scores for planning, services and specialist teams across all areas

There is strong association between characteristics

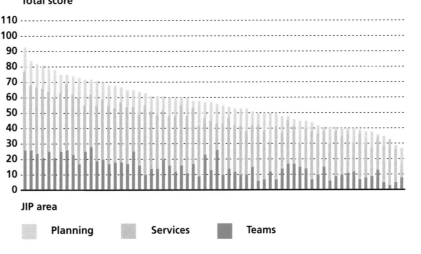

Source: Audit findings from 64 areas

7 — Priorities for action

In many areas, health and social care agencies have expressed their commitment to work together to support older people with mental health problems in their own homes or, when this is no longer appropriate, in suitable alternative accommodation. Auditors found many examples where agencies had succeeded in achieving this for older people in their areas. However, they also found that older people and their carers, in very similar circumstances, could receive quite different responses – sometimes even within the same area. If, in the future, older people with mental health problems are to receive an equally good response regardless of where they live, the following actions are priorities:

In the early stages:

1 All GPs, supported by local mental health professionals, should endeavour to diagnose mental health problems in older people as early as possible, and give them and their carers clear explanations of the problems and their likely consequences.

2 Primary care trusts and mental health trusts should ensure that all GPs and primary care staff are offered effective support and training – for example, in the use of assessment scales.

3 Health and social care agencies should provide clear information to older people and their carers about available help and benefits, using languages and media appropriate to the local population.

Once specialist help becomes necessary:

4 Health and social care agencies should ensure that their services are genuinely geared to help older people with mental health needs to live at home where appropriate, by developing home care – out of hours where necessary – with home care workers trained in mental health.

5 Agencies should collaborate to provide specialist multidisciplinary teams for older people with mental health needs including recommended core team members (consultant psychiatrists specialising in mental health problems in old age, community mental health nurses, clinical psychologists, occupational therapists, social workers).

6   Agencies should review local day provision for older people with mental health problems – looking at the range of provision in day hospitals and the amount of day care available.

7   Agencies should review with users and carers the provision of respite care.

Those who can no longer cope at home:

8   Agencies should review the environments in which mental health services are provided to make sure they are of an appropriate standard.

9   Agencies should ensure that there is sufficient residential and nursing home care of good quality available for older people with mental health problems, including some specialist provision.

10   Agencies should provide advice, support and training to the staff of residential and nursing homes.

11   Agencies should make every effort to reach a continuing care agreement, where they have not already done so.

Managing the complexity:

12   Health and social care agencies should boost team working by promoting closer working, joint assessment and care management, shared case files and compatible IT systems.

13   Agencies should develop services, which are acceptable and appropriate for black and minority ethnic communities and for younger people with dementia.

Drawing the elements together at a strategic level:

14   Agencies should work together to develop clear, agreed goals for services for older people with mental health problems, making full use of demographic and other data.

15   Agencies should develop joint plans for commissioning and delivering integrated services, based on good information and involving key partners.